STORIES
FROM THE
Bible

Introduction

The Bible is a book full of stories. In fact, it also has poems, songs, history, lists of laws, and family trees, too. And it isn't just one book. It is lots of books gathered together.

The Bible is usually thought of as having two main parts. The first is called the Old Testament. It begins at the beginning of everything, when God made the earth, the seas, the plants and animals, and people, too. It goes on to tell the story of the Jewish people and how God's plan for them worked out over hundreds of years.

After the end of the Old Testament, there is a gap of a few hundred years before the events that are described in the second main part of the Bible: the New Testament. This part is all about what happened when God sent his Son, Jesus, to teach people on earth and to show them how they can be with God always. It tells, too, about the first followers of Jesus, the first Christians, and how Jesus's message began to spread out over the whole world.

There are so many wonderful stories in the Bible that it has been hard to choose just a few to retell here. What they all have in common is that they show God at work in the world, caring for his people and helping them to turn to him.

NMAB

STORIES FROM THE
Bible

Retold by Nicola Baxter

Illustrated by Roger Langton

ARMADILLO

Published by Armadillo Books
an imprint of
Bookmart Limited
Registered Number 2372865
Trading as Bookmart Limited
Blaby Road
Wigston
Leicestershire
LE18 4SE

ISBN 1-84322-170-5

1 3 5 7 9 10 8 6 4 2

Produced for Bookmart Limited by Nicola Baxter
PO Box 215
Framingham Earl
Norwich Norfolk NR14 7UR

Designer: Amanda Hawkes
Production designer: Amy Barton

Printed in Singapore

Contents

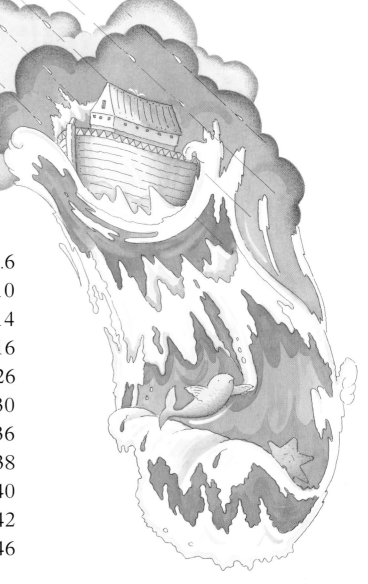

The Beginning

GENESIS 1–3

In the beginning, God made heaven and earth. At first, there was only darkness and water, but God said, "Let there be light!" and there was light. He called the light day, and he called the darkness night. That was the very first day.

Next God divided the water. He kept some below to make the seas. The rest he put up in the sky. The place between the waters he called heaven. This was on the second day.

On the third day, God moved the seas to leave areas of dry land. He made the land fruitful, so that every kind of tree and plant began to grow.

Then God put the sun and the moon and the stars in the sky. "They will show the changing seasons and the passing years," he said. This was the fourth day.

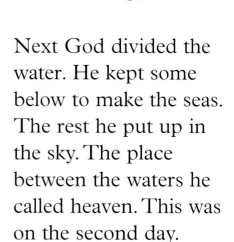

It was on the fifth day that God filled the seas and rivers with living creatures, and he made all the birds that fly in the sky.

On the sixth day, God made all the animals that live on the land, from the biggest elephant to the smallest insect.

And he made people too, to be like him and look after the earth and all the living things on it. He made a man and a woman, so that they could have children and people could fill the earth.

God looked at everything he had made and he saw that it was good. The work of creation was done. On the seventh day, God rested.

God made
a beautiful
garden for
the first man and the first
woman. It was full of plants and
trees, and a river ran through it.

God told Adam, the man,
and Eve, the woman, to
look after the garden,
which was called Eden,
but he had a warning, too.
"You can eat anything in the
garden," he said, "except the fruits
of this tree. It is the Tree of the
Knowledge of Good and Evil,
and if you eat from it, you will
certainly die."

Adam and Eve were happy in the garden, but a sly snake lived there, too. One day, it hissed to Eve, "If you eat from the Tree of the Knowledge of Good and Evil, you will not die. You will be like God, knowing everything."

The fruit looked tempting, so the woman tried some. She urged the man to eat some, too. At once, they felt different. They realized for the first time that they were not wearing clothes, so they sewed fig leaves together to cover themselves.

When Adam and Eve heard God coming, they hid. God knew at once what had happened. He told them, "Now you will have to work hard all your lives, and you will no longer live for ever."

He drove them out of Eden and put an angel with a sword of fire at the gate, so they could never return.

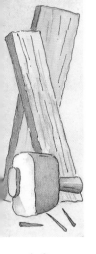

The Great Flood

GENESIS 6 : 9 – 9 : 17

Long after the time of Adam and Eve, there lived a man called Noah who had three sons: Shem Ham and Japheth. God was pleased with Noah, who tried to live a good and holy life. The same was not true of the rest of the people who lived on earth. Everywhere there was fighting and unkindness. God became sorry that he had created human beings.

One day, he said to Noah, "I am going to destroy the earth and everything on it. You must build a boat. You, your wife, your sons and their wives will all go into the boat. You can also take on board a male and a female of every kind of bird and animal and reptile, with all the food they will need to eat. You will all be saved."

God gave Noah detailed instructions about how to build the boat, called an ark. Because he was faithful to God, Noah did exactly as he had been told. Then he loaded the boat with two of every creature, just as God had said.

When the last animal and Noah's family had gone on board, Noah took his own place, and God closed the door. Soon it began to rain … and rain … and rain. It rained for forty days and forty nights. The flood water rose until there was not a scrap of land to be seen. All the creatures of the land and sky that were not on the ark were drowned.

The rain stopped at last, but it took a very long time for the flood water to go down. It was months before the tops of mountains could be seen.

Slowly, the flood continued to go down, until the ark came to rest on the top of a mountain. Then Noah opened a window and looked out. There was still water all around, so Noah sent a raven to see if she could find dry land. But the raven came back.

1 2

Noah waited. Then he sent out a dove, but she, too, returned. Another week passed. Noah sent the dove out again, and this time she came back with an olive leaf in her mouth. There must be dry land somewhere! When Noah sent the dove out for the third time, she did not come back. She had found a place to build a nest.

Then God said to Noah, "Take all the animals out of the ark. I promise never again to send a flood to destroy the earth and all the living things on it."

And God set a rainbow in the sky as a sign of his promise.

The Family of Abram

GENESIS 12 : 1–3; 15 : 1–21; 21 : 1–3; 22 : 1–18

After the great flood, Noah's sons had children – many children! Noah's descendants spread out across the world and had children of their own. After many generations, a boy called Abram was born. He grew up and married a woman called Sarai.

One day, the Lord God spoke to Abram and told him to go to a new country. "If you go where I lead you, I will bless your children and your children's children," said God, "and make you the father of a great nation."

After many years of travelling, Abram was led by God to the land of Canaan. "All the land you can see," said God, "I give to you and to your family for ever. And that family will be huge – as many people as there are stars in the sky." And God changed Abram's name to Abraham, which means "Father of Many", and changed Sarai's name to Sarah.

Both Sarah and Abraham were old by this time. They did not expect to have any children now. But God was true to his promise, and Sarah gave birth to a baby. The little boy was named Isaac.

Abraham loved Isaac with all his heart, and God decided to test whether Abraham loved God even more. He told Abraham to take Isaac to a mountain place and kill him.

Abraham's heart was heavy, but he was determined to be true to God. He took Isaac up to the mountain, built an altar of stones, and put wood on the top. Then he told the boy to lie down, and he picked up his knife.

Just at that moment, an angel called out, "Stop! You have shown that you love God." Abraham saw that a ram was caught in the bushes nearby. He gave the ram to God, and his son was saved.

Joseph and His Brothers

GENESIS 27 – 30 : 24; 37; 39 – 45; 50 : 12–13

Abraham's son Isaac grew up and in time married a girl called Rebecca, who came from Abraham's homeland. The young couple had two sons: Esau and Jacob. Many years later, when the boys had become men, Jacob tricked Isaac into blessing him as the next head of the family, even though Esau was older.

Jacob went away to escape Esau's anger. He met a girl called Rachel and worked for her father Laban for seven years for the right to marry her. But this time Jacob himself was tricked. At the wedding feast, he found it was Rachel's sister Leah whom he had married. Laban made Jacob work another seven years before he could marry Rachel as well.

Jacob had twelve sons. The first ten were called:

Reuben,   Levi,   Issachar,   Gad,   Dan,
Simeon,   Judah,   Zebulun,   Asher and Naphtali.

The last two sons were Rachel's children. They were called Joseph and Benjamin. Jacob loved these two most of all, but Joseph was his favourite. He gave the boy a beautiful, long-sleeved coat. The older brothers were jealous.

Soon Joseph began to have dreams. In the first one, he was in a field with his brothers, and each of them had a sheaf of corn. The brothers' sheaves all bowed down to Joseph's sheaf. Then Joseph dreamed of the night sky. In his dream, the sun and the moon and eleven stars bowed down to him. When he told his brothers about these dreams, they hated him even more.

One day, Joseph's brothers were away from home looking after their father's sheep. Jacob sent Joseph to see how they were getting on. When they saw him approaching, out in the countryside where no one could see, Joseph's brothers decided to do away with him once and for all.

Only Reuben disagreed. "Let's not kill him," he said. "We will throw him into a pit and leave him here." Reuben hoped to be able to come back and rescue Joseph later.

So the brothers tore off Joseph's coat and threw him into a pit. A little later, some merchants passed on their way to Egypt. Judah had an idea. "Let's sell Joseph," he said. "We shouldn't kill our own flesh and blood." Joseph was sold for twenty pieces of silver.

Then the brothers tore the special coat and dipped it in a goat's blood. They took it back to Jacob and pretended that Joseph had been killed by a wild animal. The old man was devastated by the loss of his favourite son. He vowed never to forget him.

Meanwhile, Joseph was beginning a new life in Egypt. He was sold to Potiphar, the captain of Pharaoh's guard. Joseph did well and worked hard. Potiphar trusted him and put him in charge of his whole household and all his property. Everything did well under Joseph's care.

Now Joseph was a good-looking young man, and Potiphar's wife took a fancy to him. Joseph was loyal to his master and tried to avoid being alone with her, but this made the woman angry. She told her husband that Joseph had tried to take advantage of her. Potiphar was furious that his trust, as he thought, had been betrayed. He sent Joseph to prison.

Once again, Joseph's honesty stood him in good stead. The prison governor recognized his qualities and put him in charge of the prisoners. Some time later, Pharaoh's butler and baker offended him, and he threw them into gaol. Joseph, of course, had charge of them.

One day, Joseph noticed that the two looked worried and asked why. They explained that they had each had a dream the night before, but they were puzzled by what the dreams meant.

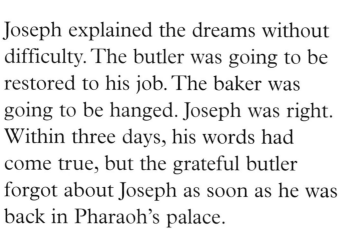

Joseph explained the dreams without difficulty. The butler was going to be restored to his job. The baker was going to be hanged. Joseph was right. Within three days, his words had come true, but the grateful butler forgot about Joseph as soon as he was back in Pharaoh's palace.

Nearly two years passed before something happened that reminded the butler of Joseph. Pharaoh himself had two vivid dreams. He dreamed of seven plump cows and seven starving cows by a riverbank. The starving cows ate the sleek ones. Then he dreamed of seven thin ears of corn swallowing up seven fat ones.

Pharaoh sent for all the wisest men in the kingdom, but none of them could tell him what the dreams meant. Then the butler remembered the Hebrew slave who had helped him years before, and Joseph was summoned to Pharaoh's palace.

"The dreams both mean the same thing," said Joseph. "God is showing you the future. There will be seven years of good harvests and plenty for everyone, followed by seven years when the crops fail and there is a terrible famine. If you take steps to store food now, you can avoid the worst of the disaster."

Joseph suggested that Pharaoh should appoint a clever and honest man to oversee the planning. It didn't take Pharaoh long to realize that Joseph himself was the man for the job.

So, at the age of thirty, Joseph became the most powerful man in Egypt after Pharaoh. He carried out the plan through the seven good years, and when the seven years of famine came, Egypt was the only country in the region to have food.

Back in Canaan, the famine was severe. Jacob, Joseph's father, said to his sons, "I hear they have corn in Egypt. Go down and buy some to keep us going." The ten eldest sons set off, leaving Benjamin behind.

When his brothers appeared before him, Joseph recognized them at once, but they saw only a powerful Egyptian. Joseph did not reveal himself, but pretended to believe that the brothers were spies. "I will put one of you in prison," he said. "The others must go to Canaan and bring back your youngest brother. Then I will believe your story."

"We are being punished for what we did to Joseph," said Reuben. Joseph overheard him and wept secretly at these words.

While Simeon stayed in prison, the other brothers took their corn and went back to Jacob. Secretly, Joseph put the money they had paid in the sacks with the corn. On the journey, the brothers discovered this and were puzzled.

Jacob was reluctant to let Benjamin go, but he agreed at last. He sent gifts to Joseph and double the amount of silver first paid. He thought that a mistake had been made and did not want to anger the powerful man who held their lives in his hands.

When the brothers arrived in Egypt, Joseph treated them kindly, even inviting them for a meal. It was an emotional time for him, seeing his much loved younger brother but not revealing who he was.

Once again, when the brothers left, Joseph played a trick on them. This time, not only did he replace their money, but he also hid a precious silver cup in Benjamin's luggage.

The brothers had not gone far when some of Joseph's men came after them. They found the cup and took the party back to the city.

Joseph pretended to be furious and demanded that Benjamin be left behind to become his slave. "My lord, the loss of his son would kill our father," pleaded Judah, and at this Joseph could keep up the pretence no longer. Sending out his Egyptian servants, he told his brothers who he was. Of course, everyone cried and hugged and cried again. It was wonderful!

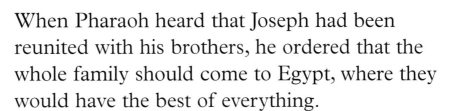

When Pharaoh heard that Joseph had been reunited with his brothers, he ordered that the whole family should come to Egypt, where they would have the best of everything.

Jacob could hardly believe his ears when the news was brought to him. "My son is alive!" he cried. "I shall see him before I die."

So it was that Jacob's family settled in Egypt. Jacob was an old man, and, when he died, his sons did as they had promised and took his body back to Canaan for burial.

The Baby in the Bulrushes

EXODUS 1 : 7–22; 2 : 1–25; 3 : 1–17; 4 : 13–18

After Joseph died, the Israelites did well in Egypt. Their numbers increased until the new Pharaoh began to be afraid. "If there was a war," he said, "they might side with our enemies and overrun us."

So Pharaoh made life very difficult for the Israelites. He forced them to work hard, making bricks and building new cities. But still there were more and more Israelites.

Then Pharaoh ordered that all baby boys born to the Israelites should be drowned in the river. Girls would be allowed to live to become slaves.

But one Israelite woman, when she gave birth to a fine boy, was determined he should live. When he grew too big to hide in the house, she made him a cradle from bulrushes.

She painted the outside with pitch, so that it would be waterproof. Then she placed the cradle, with the baby inside, among the reeds beside the river. The baby's sister, Miriam, watched from a distance.

Soon Pharaoh's daughter came down to the river with her maids. She saw the cradle and asked for it to be brought to her. She knew at once that the baby inside was Hebrew.

Miriam could see that Pharaoh's daughter was not going to harm the baby. "Would you like me to find someone to look after him for you?" she asked. So it was that the baby's own mother took care of him. When he was old enough, she took him to Pharaoh's daughter, who adopted him and named him Moses.

28

Although Moses grew up in an Egyptian family, he never forgot who he was. One day, when he was grown up, he saw some Israelites doing the heavy work they were always given. As he watched, an Egyptian hit one of the Israelite slaves.

Moses looked around. No one was watching. He struck the Egyptian, killing him, and hid his body in the sand.

Moses thought he was safe, but what he did soon became known. Pharaoh tried to have him put to death, but Moses escaped and went to live in Midian, where he married a girl called Zipporah.

Years passed. Pharaoh died, but the Israelites were still slaves. Then God, remembering his promise to Abraham, took action.

One day, Moses was on a mountainside when he saw something extraordinary. It was a bush that was on fire, as sometimes happened in the heat, but although the flames flickered, the bush did not burn.

Then God spoke to Moses out of the fire and said, "I have seen the suffering of my people in Egypt. I am going to send you to Pharaoh, and you will bring them to a land flowing with milk and honey."

Moses was not sure. Could he speak well enough to convince anyone to follow him? God promised that Moses's brother Aaron would help him. So Moses set off for Egypt.

Escape from Egypt

Aaron met Moses on his journey. Together they gathered the chief men of Israel and told them of God's plan. Then Moses and Aaron went to Pharaoh and told him that God wanted the Israelites to be freed. But Pharaoh would not hear of it. Instead, he made the Hebrew slaves work even harder.

So God sent Moses to Pharaoh again and told him to hold out his staff over the River Nile. At once the river, and all the water in the kingdom, turned to blood. Pharaoh was not impressed.

Then God sent a plague of frogs to Egypt. There were frogs everywhere, even in people's beds! Still Pharaoh would not let the Israelites go.

After that, God sent more plagues to Egypt. First there were maggots everywhere, then flies, then all the camels, cattle, sheep and asses became ill and died. Next, people and animals were covered with horrible sores. As Pharaoh still would not agree, God sent a violent hailstorm that flattened crops and trees. In all of this the Israelites and their animals were not harmed.

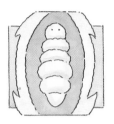   

When Pharaoh still did not change his mind, Moses became desperate, but God sent a plague of locusts across the land. Even that did not work, so God made Egypt dark for three days and three nights. Only the Israelites had light in the daytime.

It was no use. God sent Moses to Pharaoh with one last warning. "At midnight the firstborn child of every family will die," he said.

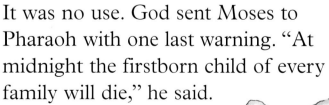

Moses called together all the chief men of the Israelites and told them what they must do.

"Tonight, each family must kill a lamb to eat," he said. "You can have unleavened bread and bitter herbs with it. Mark the top and sides of your doorways with the lamb's blood and make sure that you do not go outside until morning. That way, when the angel of the Lord passes through to kill all the firstborn Egyptians, he will know to pass over your houses. And you must be ready to leave Egypt at a moment's notice."

Then Moses told the Israelites that this night would be remembered for ever. "It will be called the Passover," he said, "because the angel passed over your homes, and it will always be a special sign between you and God."

It happened just as Moses had said. At midnight, every firstborn child of the Egyptians died, even in Pharaoh's own family, but the Israelites were safe.

Before dawn, Pharaoh sent for Moses and Aaron. "Go," he said, "and take all your flocks and herds with you. Go and worship your God as you wish!"

The Israelites quickly gathered up all their belongings and set off. After four hundred and thirty years, they came out of Egypt, free at last.

The country they had to travel through was wild and empty, but God led them, appearing as a pillar of cloud by day and a pillar of fire by night.

Meanwhile, Pharaoh was having a change of heart.
He realized that he needed the Israelite slaves.
With hundreds of chariots and soldiers,
he set off after the Israelites.

Moses and his people
were camped near the
sea when they saw the
great army coming after
them. Some were very
frightened, but God
told Moses to hold out
his staff over the water.
A strong wind blew, and
the sea parted, leaving a
path between great walls
of water.

The Israelites went through safely, but the
Egyptians' chariot wheels got stuck and they were
slow to cross. Then, with all the Israelites safely on
the far side, God told Moses to stretch out his staff
one more time. At once, the waters rushed back,
and all the Egyptians were drowned.

So Moses led the Israelites away from Egypt, but it was not an easy job. The Israelites were worried and frightened. They did not know what would happen and often wondered if they should have stayed in Egypt.

Yet each time there was a problem, God showed them what to do. "If you listen to me and do what I say, I will never bring suffering to you as I did to the Egyptians," God told his people.

There was little to eat in the bare lands they travelled through, but God helped the Israelites again. One morning, they found the ground covered in tiny white flakes. It was a kind of food and it tasted good, a little bit sweet like honey. They called it manna.

Another time, the travellers were thirsty and there was no water to be found. God told Moses to strike a rock with his staff. At once water came gushing out.

The Ten Commandments

EXODUS 19 – 20; 25 : 1–9; 32 : 1–20; DEUTERONOMY 31 : 1–2, 7–8; 34 : 1–5

During the time that the Israelites were in the desert, God spoke to them in many different ways. Once, when they were camped at the foot of a mountain called Sinai, Moses climbed up to the top. There God told him that he was to receive something very special.

Three days later, a thick cloud covered the top of Mount Sinai. Thunder rumbled and lightning flashed. Then, as the people waited, trembling, at the bottom, Moses went up once more.

God gave Moses ten commandments, or rules, for the people to follow. They were written on slabs of stone.

1. You must only follow the one, true God.
2. Do not make false gods.
3. Do not misuse God's name.
4. Keep the Sabbath day special.
5. Love and respect your father and mother.
6. Do not kill.
7. Be faithful to your husband or wife.
8. Do not steal.
9. Do not tell lies.
10. Do not be jealous or greedy.

God told Moses to have a special box made to keep the commandments in. It would be called the Ark of the Covenant.

Moses had been on the mountain a long time, listening to God, and down below the Israelites had become tired of waiting. Moses had left his brother Aaron in charge. The people persuaded him to make them a god. They didn't know if Moses would ever come back. So Aaron melted down all the gold he could find and made a huge golden calf for the people to worship.

When Moses came down at last and saw this, he was furious. He hurled the calf into the fire and reminded the Israelites about their one, true God. Once more, they promised to listen to Moses and obey God, but in the years that followed, they often forgot. Moses was old now. He chose a man called Joshua to be the new leader. God led Moses to a high place so he could look out over Canaan. Then, having seen the promised land, Moses died.

The Promised Land

JOSHUA 2 : 1–24; 6

For forty long years, the Israelites were without a home. The land of Canaan had been promised to them by God, but there were already people living there. Now, with Joshua as their leader, it was time to enter their land at last.

Joshua knew that the people living in Canaan would not give it up without a fight. He decided to attack the city of Jericho first and sent out spies to see how strong it was.

The spies went to the house of a woman called Rahab. When the King's men came looking for them, she hid them on the roof. The spies realized that although the city walls were very strong, the people inside were afraid of the Israelites.

"Tie a red cord to your window and stay inside," they told Rahab. "We promise that when we attack, you and your family will be safe."

Then God told Joshua how to attack the city. Each day for six days, the Israelites marched round the city in silence except for the sound of rams'-horn trumpets. On the seventh day, Joshua gave a signal. Suddenly all the men shouted, and the trumpets sounded. The noise was enormous … and the walls of Jericho fell down!

This was just the first of Joshua's battles. It wasn't easy, but in the end he captured the whole of the land of Canaan. He divided the land so that each of the twelve tribes of Israel, descended from Jacob's twelve sons, had its own area. The Israelites were in their own land at last.

Samson and Delilah

JUDGES 16: 4–30

Over the years, many enemies tried to take the Israelites' land away again. At one time, because the Israelites were not living as they should, God allowed people called the Philistines to overcome them. Things were very difficult for the Israelites for many years.

At last, God chose a man to begin to set the Israelites free. His name was Samson, and he was very, very strong. He liked to fight, and killed a lion with his bare hands, as well as many Philistines. No one was strong enough to stop him.

One day, Samson fell in love. The girl's name was Delilah. Samson's enemies saw their chance. They promised Delilah lots of money if she could find out where her husband's strength came from.

At first, Samson teased Delilah, but she didn't give up. She asked and asked, until at last Samson told her the truth. "My hair has never been cut," he said. "If my head was shaved, I'd be like any other man."

So Delilah lulled Samson to sleep. She got a Philistine to shave off Samson's hair. When he awoke, the Philistines overpowered him easily. They blinded Samson and threw him into prison.

The Philistines held a great celebration in their temple. All the important people were there. They called for Samson to be brought in so that they could make fun of him. They didn't notice that, while he was in prison, Samson's hair had begun to grow.

Samson stood between the great pillars of the temple and prayed to God. "Let me die with the Philistines!" he cried, and he pushed with all his might. The pillars fell. The roof crashed down. Everyone in the temple was killed.

The Kings of Israel

1 SAMUEL 1 : 10–28; 3 : 1–18; 8 : 4–6; 9 : 1–27; 10 : 1; 16 : 1, 14–21; 17 : 1–52

There was once a woman called Hannah who longed to have a baby. Her husband already had children, so he was not so worried. Hannah prayed in the temple. She promised God that if she had a son, she would bring him to the temple to serve God all his life.

Before long, Hannah did have a baby boy. She called him Samuel. Although she loved him very much, she did not forget her promise. When Samuel was still a small boy, she brought him to live in the temple. A priest called Eli took care of him.

One night, Samuel heard someone call his name. He thought it was Eli, but the old priest had not called. Three times Samuel heard the voice. Then both he and Eli realized it was God who was calling. Samuel went back to his bed on the floor. Next time God called his name, he answered, "Your servant is listening."

What Samuel had to hear was not good news for Eli. God told the boy that the priest and his family were to be punished for things that Eli's sons had done. Samuel didn't want to have to tell the old man, but when he did, Eli simply said, "The Lord must do what he knows is right."

Samuel grew up and became an important man. Everything happened as God had said. There was more trouble with the Philistines. Eli's sons were killed in battle, and the old priest died. Then everything settled down again. The Israelites listened to God once more, and Samuel ruled over them as a judge, wisely and well.

But the Israelites never were content for long. Samuel was getting old, and the people wanted a king. "Other people have kings," they said.

God chose a man called Saul to be king. Samuel put oil on his head as a sign that God had chosen him. At first, all went well, but soon Saul began to do what he liked, not what God wanted.

"I have chosen another king," God told Samuel. It was a boy called David from Bethlehem. He was only a shepherd, but God had great plans for him.

44

Only God and Samuel knew that David would one day be king, but David was soon to meet Saul. The king was often ill. Only music made him feel better. David could sing and play the harp beautifully. He was called to play to Saul whenever the king was ill.

Before long, Saul had other troubles. The Philistines were once more on the attack. Soon the Philistine army and the Israelite army were facing each other across a valley. The Philistines had a famous fighter called Goliath, a giant of a man. Each day he challenged the Israelites to fight him. No one dared to step forward.

Then, one day, David happened to be taking food to his brothers, who were in the Israelite army. He heard the challenge. "How dare this man challenge God's people?" he cried. "I will fight him!"

To everyone's amazement, David went out to fight Goliath. He was not trained in fighting and would not even wear armour, but he was used to using his shepherd's sling to protect his father's sheep. He put a stone in the sling and hurled it at Goliath, hitting him on the forehead. The Philistine was dead!

Filled with courage, the Israelites attacked the army facing them and drove it away.

David lived in the palace now. He was great friends with Saul's son Jonathan. But Saul could see that David was a much greater man than he was himself. He began to hate David and planned to kill him.

Then Saul had more trouble from the Philistines. In the end, Jonathan was killed in battle. Saul himself was wounded and took his own life. In spite of everything that had happened, David was very sad.

In time, David became king. He captured Jerusalem for the Israelites and made it their capital. It was known as "the city of David". David was a powerful ruler, but he, too, grew old. When he died, his son Solomon became king.

God made Solomon wise, rich and powerful. To show his love for God, Solomon had a great temple built in Jerusalem. It was a wonderful building, made of wood and stone and gold. There was a special place inside for the Ark of the Covenant. The temple made the Israelites proud and happy.

Warnings from God

1 KINGS 17; JONAH

Solomon ruled wisely and well for a long time, but in the end even he turned from God. After he died, the kingdom of Israel was divided. One part was still called Israel, and the other part was called Judah.

Sometimes the two kingdoms worked together. Sometimes they were enemies. During this time, a few men tried to remind the Israelites and their kings about God. These men were called prophets.

The first great prophet, Elijah, had to run for his life when he took a message from God to King Ahab. The king was furious. Elijah hid in a rocky place, and God sent ravens with food for him.

More and more enemies attacked both the kingdoms. First the Assyrians and then the Babylonians conquered them. Many Jewish people were taken away to other lands. Finally, the Persians swept in and took over. King Cyrus let the Jews return to Jerusalem. They rebuilt the temple, which had been destroyed.

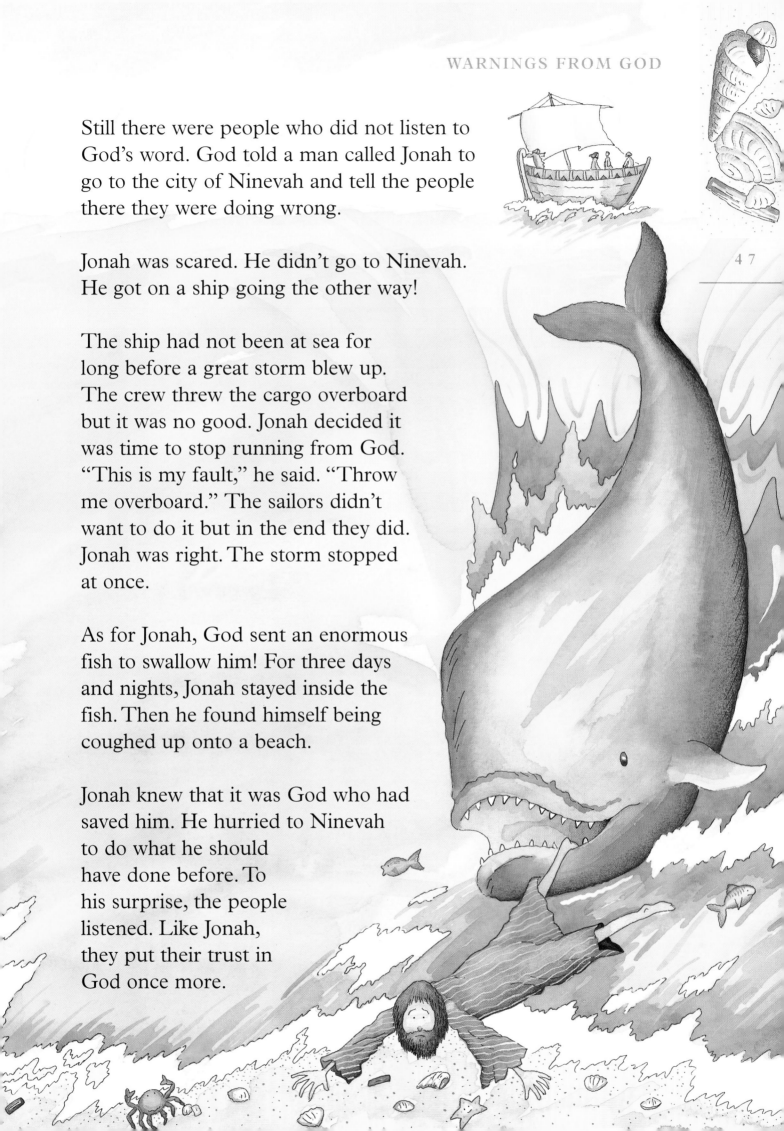

Still there were people who did not listen to God's word. God told a man called Jonah to go to the city of Ninevah and tell the people there they were doing wrong.

Jonah was scared. He didn't go to Ninevah. He got on a ship going the other way!

The ship had not been at sea for long before a great storm blew up. The crew threw the cargo overboard but it was no good. Jonah decided it was time to stop running from God. "This is my fault," he said. "Throw me overboard." The sailors didn't want to do it but in the end they did. Jonah was right. The storm stopped at once.

As for Jonah, God sent an enormous fish to swallow him! For three days and nights, Jonah stayed inside the fish. Then he found himself being coughed up onto a beach.

Jonah knew that it was God who had saved him. He hurried to Ninevah to do what he should have done before. To his surprise, the people listened. Like Jonah, they put their trust in God once more.

The Birth of Jesus

LUKE 1 : 26 – 2 : 7; MATTHEW 1 : 18–25

In Nazareth, a small town in Gallilee, there lived a young woman called Mary. She was engaged to a man called Joseph, a carpenter. One day, an angel appeared to Mary. "Don't be afraid," the angel said. "I have come to tell you that you are going to have a baby. He will be called Jesus, and he will be king over Israel for ever and ever."

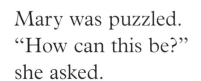

Mary was puzzled. "How can this be?" she asked.

"The baby will be the Son of God," the angel explained. "I can also tell you that your cousin Elizabeth is going to have a baby too, even though she is no longer young. God's promises always come true."

"I am God's servant," Mary replied. "I am ready for whatever he asks of me."

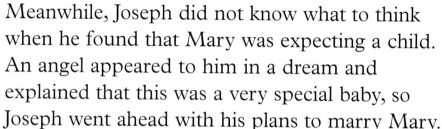

Mary hurried to visit Elizabeth. It was all true! Elizabeth was pregnant, and she felt the baby jump with joy inside her when Mary arrived.

In time, Elizabeth gave birth to a son. He was called John. His father Zechariah foretold that John would prepare the way for the Son of God.

Meanwhile, Joseph did not know what to think when he found that Mary was expecting a child. An angel appeared to him in a dream and explained that this was a very special baby, so Joseph went ahead with his plans to marry Mary.

When it was close to the time that Mary's baby would be born, Emperor Augustus decided that each man should go back to his family's home town to be put on a register. That meant that Joseph had to go to Bethlehem.

When Joseph and Mary arrived, they had to sleep in a stable because there was no other room. It was there that Jesus was born.

Visitors from Near and Far

LUKE 2 : 8–20; MATTHEW 2 : 1–14

On the night that Jesus was born, shepherds were watching their flocks on the lonely hills around Bethlehem. Suddenly, the darkness was filled with a bright, shining light. It was an angel!

"Don't be afraid," said the angel. "I have brought you wonderful news. Today in Bethlehem a baby has been born who will save the world. You will find him there in a stable."

And the whole sky was suddenly filled with angels singing and praising God.

As the light of the angels faded, the shepherds gathered their cloaks around them and set off for Bethlehem.

To their amazement, the shepherds found Joseph, Mary and the baby in a stable, just as the angel had said. Later, they could not help telling everyone they met what they had heard and seen that night. As for Mary, she quietly thought about what had happened and what it might mean.

Far away in the east, other travellers had seen an extraordinary star in the sky. They were wise men, who believed that it showed that a new King of the Jews had been born. They set off to find him.

But when King Herod heard of the visitors, he was worried. "Please do find this new King," he said, "and make sure you let me know where he is."

The wise men followed the star until it stopped over the place where Jesus had been born. Filled with joy, the wise men went inside and bowed low in front of the baby. They gave him presents of gold, frankincense and myrrh.

Before they set off for home, the wise men had a dream. It warned them not to tell Herod what they had found, so they went another way.

The danger was not over. Joseph also had a dream. An angel told him to take his little family to Egypt, where it would be safe from Herod. Joseph didn't waste time. That very night he led Mary and Jesus away. They stayed in Egypt until Herod was dead, before returning at last to Nazareth.

Jesus grew up, healthy and strong, and he was wise, too.

Each year, Mary and Joseph went to Jerusalem for the Passover festival. When Jesus was twelve, they took him with them. On the way home, they assumed the boy was travelling with other members of the party, but at nightfall, when they could not find him, they became very worried.

Mary and Joseph returned to Jerusalem and spent three days desperately searching. When they found their son at last, an extraordinary scene met their eyes. Jesus was sitting in the temple, surrounded by teachers, and *they* were learning from *him*!

"What are you doing?" gasped Mary. "Don't you understand how worried we've been?"

But Jesus's answer was simple. "You should have known I'd be in my Father's house," he said. He understood that he was the Son of God.

John the Baptist

MATTHEW 3 : 1–18; 4 : 1–17

John, the son of Elizabeth and Zechariah, and Jesus's cousin, grew up to be a holy man. He lived alone in wild places, listening to the word of God. He ate what he could find, such as locusts and wild honey, and he dressed in animal skins. One day, he understood what God wanted him to do.

John came down to the River Jordan and began to preach and to baptize people. This meant that they were dipped in the water of the river as a sign that they were sorry for their sins and wanted them to be washed away so that they could start afresh.

The preacher's words and actions were so powerful that some people wondered if he was the Son of God. But John said, "Someone is coming who is much greater than me. I am not worthy even to undo his sandals."

One day, Jesus himself arrived with the crowds who came to be baptized. He was a grown man now. "You should be baptizing me!" John protested, but Jesus was sure. John pushed him gently under the water. As Jesus came up again, it seemed as if the heavens opened and the Spirit of God seemed to settle on Jesus like a dove. "This is my Son, my loved and chosen one," said a voice from on high.

Then Jesus, too, felt the need to be alone. He went into the desert for forty days and forty nights. During this time, the devil tempted him. "If you are the Son of God," he said, "you can make bread out of these stones. Nothing can harm you. You can rule the world!"

But Jesus stood firm in his faith in God. In the end, the devil left him, and Jesus left Nazareth to settle in Capernaum, on the Sea of Gallilee. It was time for his work to begin.

The Twelve Disciples

MARK 1 : 14–20; 29–31; 3 : 13–19

Jesus began to teach the people about God. One day he was walking by the Sea of Galilee when he saw two fisherman at work. They were Simon and his brother Andrew.
"Come with me," said Jesus, "and I will make you fishers of men."
Simon and Andrew didn't hesitate. They put down their nets and followed Jesus.

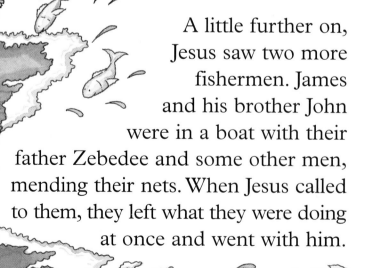

A little further on, Jesus saw two more fishermen. James and his brother John were in a boat with their father Zebedee and some other men, mending their nets. When Jesus called to them, they left what they were doing at once and went with him.

As Jesus travelled, talking about God, amazing
things began to happen. For example,
when Jesus visited Simon's and
Andrew's home, he found
Simon's mother-in-law
in bed with a fever.
Jesus stretched out
his hand and helped
her up. At once, she
felt completely better!

News that Jesus could
heal people spread fast.
Soon there was a huge
crowd wherever he went.

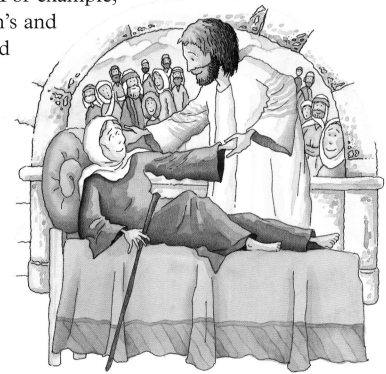

As he went about teaching and healing,
Jesus found more disciples to follow him.
He didn't only choose people who led good,
respectable lives. "Well people don't need a doctor,"
he said. "I've come to help those who really need me."

In all, Jesus chose twelve men to be his special followers.

Simon,   Andrew,   James,   John,   Philip,   Nathaniel*,   Matthew,   Thomas,
another James,   Thaddeus,   another Simon   and Judas Iscariot.

*or Bartholomew

Jesus's Miracles

JOHN 2 : 1–11; MARK 4 : 35–41;
LUKE 9 : 12–17

News about Jesus spread very quickly. He was a teacher of great power. He could heal the sick. And, it seemed, he could do other extraordinary things.

Jesus's first miracle took place at a wedding. Mary, Jesus's mother, was there. Jesus and all the disciples were also invited.

During the celebrations, all the wine was drunk! There was nothing left for the guests, and Mary was afraid that this would spoil the party. She told her son, hoping he would be able to do something. She told the servants to do whatever he asked.

Jesus made the servants fill all the wine jars to the brim with water. When they poured some of the water into a cup, they found that it had turned into wine.

It wasn't just any old wine either! It was much better than the first lot that had been served.

Jesus's disciples saw what had happened. They felt even more strongly that he was a very special man. Other people felt this, too. Jesus was surrounded by people wherever he went. At the end of one busy day, hoping to escape from the crowds, he and his disciples got into a fishing boat and sailed out on to the Sea of Galilee. Jesus fell asleep.

Suddenly, a huge storm blew up. The disciples were very afraid, but Jesus stood up and spoke to the storm! "Peace!" he said. "Be still!" At once the wind dropped and the waves became calm. The disciples were amazed. "Even the wind and the waves do what he says!" they gasped.

No matter what Jesus did to try to find a quiet place to rest and speak with his disciples, the crowds who longed to see him seemed to find him. They followed him for miles, even to the loneliest places.

60

Once, when Jesus had been curing sick people among the crowd, it grew late. The disciples were worried. "Tell everyone to go," they told Jesus. "We are miles from anywhere here, it is nearly night, and there is hardly anything for all these people to eat."

"They don't need to go. You can feed them. What is there?" asked Jesus.

"Just five loaves of bread and two fishes," said the disciples. "But there are five thousand people here!"

Jesus took the loaves and fishes and blessed them. Then he told the disciples to ask the people to sit down and to divide the food between them. To their astonishment, not only was there plenty for everyone, but twelve big baskets of scraps were picked up afterwards.

After the meal, the crowds gradually broke up and went home. Jesus sent his disciples across the Sea of Galilee in a boat, while he went up a nearby hillside to pray.

From the hill, Jesus could see the disciples' boat far out in the water. They were struggling to row against a wind blowing in their faces.

Suddenly, the disciples spotted a figure walking towards them in the moonlight. It seemed to be walking on the water!

"It's a ghost!" they cried, terrified.

"It is I! Don't be afraid!" called Jesus. Simon, whom Jesus had named Simon Peter, shouted out. "If it's really you, let me walk on the water, too!"

"Come!" called Jesus, and Peter stepped out onto the water. He took a few steps, but then he became afraid and began to sink. "Save me!" he cried.

Jesus stretched out his arms and caught Simon Peter. "You have so little faith," he told him.

The disciples knelt down. "It's true. You are the Son of God," they told Jesus.

61

Jesus's Teaching

LUKE 10 : 25–37; 15 : 3–7;
MATTHEW 19 : 13–15; LUKE 8 : 4–15

Jesus taught his followers about God by what he did and by what he said. He told stories with special meanings. They are called parables.

One day a lawyer asked what he must do to live for ever with God. "What does the Jewish law say?" asked Jesus.

"I must love God with all my heart and all my soul and all my strength," the man replied, "and I must care as much about my neighbour as I do about myself."

"That's right," said Jesus.

"But who is my neighbour?" the man wanted to know.

Jesus told this story. A man was making a journey from Jerusalem to Jericho when he was attacked by robbers. They took everything he had and left him half dead beside the road.

A little while later, a priest walked past on the other side, but he didn't stop to help the man.

Later still, a Levite came along. He was a man who served God in the temple, but he didn't stop either.

At last a Samaritan, whose people were not generally friendly to the Jews, came by. He at once helped the man who had been attacked. When he had bandaged his wounds, he put him on his own donkey and took him to an inn. The next day, when the Samaritan had to go on his way, he even left money so that the recovering man could be looked after.

"Now," said Jesus, "who was a real neighbour to the man who was hurt?"

"The one who helped him," said the lawyer.

"Go and do the same," Jesus replied. It was his way of explaining that everyone is our neighbour, no matter who he or she is.

Another time, Jesus told a story about a shepherd who had a hundred sheep. One evening, when he counted them, he only had ninety-nine!

Did the shepherd just forget about the missing sheep? No! He made sure the rest were safe and went to look for the one that was lost. And he kept searching until he found it. Then he hurried home with it on his shoulders, telling everyone how happy he was.

"The shepherd was happier about the one sheep he found again than about the ninety-nine that were always there," said Jesus. "That's how God feels when someone leaves their bad ways and turns to him."

Jesus acted just as he taught. Everyone was important to him. Once, when some families with children wanted to see him, the disciples turned them away, but Jesus said, "Let the little children come to me. The Kingdom of Heaven belongs to little ones like this."

Jesus told a story about his teaching, too. He said that a man went out to sow some seed. In those days it was done by hand. As the man threw the seed, some fell onto a footpath, where it was trampled by passers-by.

Some fell on rock, where plants that grew shrivelled up and died, and some fell among weeds, which grew up and smothered the young plants. But the seed that fell on good soil grew and a hundred times as much seed was gathered from it.

"The seed is the word of God," Jesus said. "Some people listen to it, believe in it and try to live life as God wishes. This is like seed falling on good soil. They will have a wonderful harvest."

As Jesus talked and taught, more and more people believed that he really was the Son of God. The chief priests and other important people were worried by this. They began to plot against Jesus. And Jesus himself knew that his time on Earth was coming to an end.

Jesus in Jerusalem

MATTHEW 21 : 1–17

The time of Passover was coming, when many Jews went to Jerusalem. Knowing that he was likely to be arrested, Jesus set out as well with his twelve disciples.

When they reached the outskirts of a little village just outside Jerusalem, Jesus stopped. "Go into the village," he told his disciples, and you will see a young donkey that has never been ridden. Bring it to me. If anyone asks you what you are doing, say, 'Our Master needs it'"

The disciples found everything just as Jesus had said. They came back with the donkey and threw their cloaks over it for Jesus to ride. So, mounted on the donkey, Jesus rode into Jerusalem.

The welcome he received was amazing. People lined the streets, waving palm branches and calling, "Hosanna! Blessed is he that comes in the name of the Lord! God bless the King of Israel!"

Of course, Jesus went to the temple. What he found there made him very angry. There were money-changers doing business and traders selling all sorts of goods. This was not treating the temple as God's house!

Jesus knocked over the money-changers tables, sending coins flying. "Holy writings say that the temple should be a place of prayer," he cried. "You have made it into a den of thieves!"

The Last Supper

MARK 14 : 12–25; 32–46; 15 : 1–39

Jesus knew that the time was coming when he must leave his life on Earth to join his Father in heaven. The chief priests were keen to stop Jesus's work.

Around this time, the devil put the idea of betraying his master into the mind of Judas Iscariot, one of Jesus's disciples. Judas told the chief priests that he could lead them to Jesus, so that he could be arrested when there were no crowds about to protect him. The chief priests were delighted and promised Judas thirty pieces of silver if he would do as he had said.

On the first day of the Festival o Passover, Jesus's disciples asked h where they would eat their specia Passover meal.

Jesus told Peter and John to look sign near the gates of Jerusalem. "When you see a man carrying a of water on his head," he said, "f him. He will take you to the hous where we will eat tonight."

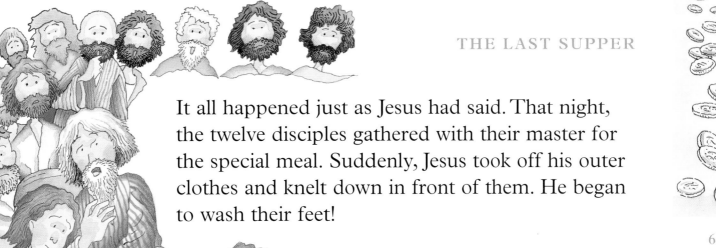

It all happened just as Jesus had said. That night, the twelve disciples gathered with their master for the special meal. Suddenly, Jesus took off his outer clothes and knelt down in front of them. He began to wash their feet!

Some of the disciples were shocked. "Don't!" they said. "That's a servant's job! You are our master!"

"Yes, I am," said Jesus, "but I am setting you an example. You should take care of each other as I have taken care of you."

Jesus began to prepare his followers for what would soon happen. He shared bread with them, saying, "This is my body." Then he passed around a cup of wine, saying, "This is my blood." The disciples were worried. Jesus said, "I will not be with you much longer. You must love one another as I have loved you."

After supper, Jesus and his followers went out in the darkness to the Garden of Gethsemane. Jesus told the disciples to wait while he went a little further on to pray. Jesus spoke to God his Father. "If my suffering is the only way," he said, "may your will be done."

When Jesus returned to his disciples, they were fast asleep! Suddenly, the garden was full of people. One man stepped forward. It was Judas. With a kiss, he showed the soldiers sent by the chief priests which man was Jesus.

Weapons were not needed. Jesus allowed himself to be arrested. The disciples were afraid and ran away.

Jesus was dragged before several officials. The chief priests were looking for someone to sentence him to death. But Pontius Pilate, the Roman governor, could find no reason to do so. At last, seeing that a huge crowd had gathered, demanding Jesus's death, Pilate gave them a choice. "Shall I free Jesus or the murderer Barabbas?" he asked. "Barabbas!" yelled the crowd. Pilate was afraid to go against them. Jesus would be crucified – hung on a cross to die.

On the day of his execution, Jesus had to carry his own heavy cross to a hill outside Jerusalem.

He was nailed to the cross. Two thieves, who were also sentenced to die that day, hung on either side of him.

Jesus was in great pain. He called out to God.

"Father, forgive them," he said. "They don't understand what they are doing."

Below the cross, Mary, Jesus's mother, watched helplessly. John, one of the disciples, comforted her.

At last Jesus died. The sky was dark, and it was as if the whole Earth shuddered. Even a Roman soldier realized that something important had happened. "This man really was the Son of God," he said.

The First Easter

15 : 42–47; JOHN 20 : 1–21;
ACTS 1 : 9–11; 2 : 1–4, 42–47

Jesus was put to death on a Friday. Later that day, his body was taken down from the cross. A rich man called Joseph of Arimathea arranged for Jesus's body to be wrapped in a sheet and laid in a rock tomb. It was in a garden, and Joseph had planned to use it for his own burial.

Joseph rolled a large stone across the entrance of the tomb. Sadly, Jesus's friends and disciples left the garden.

Pilate had heard rumours that Jesus would rise from the dead, so he sent soldiers to guard the tomb. But very early on Sunday morning, an angel came and rolled away the stone. Terrified, the soldiers ran away.

A little later, Mary Magdalene and some other women came to visit the tomb. They found it open, and Jesus's body was gone! They were frightened. Mary Magdalene ran back to find Peter and John.

As the other women stood there, two angels appeared. "Jesus is not here," they said. "He is alive again!"

The women rushed back to find the disciples. Meanwhile, Mary Magdalene returned with Peter and John. The two men went into the tomb. Happiness filled them as they realized that Jesus's words had come true. He really was alive!

73

Mary Magdalene stayed in the garden. Suddenly she saw a man standing beside her.

"Why are you crying?" he asked.

Mary thought he must be the gardener and begged him to tell her what he had done with Jesus's body, but the man said just one word, "Mary!"

Then Mary realized that it was Jesus himself who was standing in front of her. She was overjoyed.

Back in Jerusalem, some of the disciples found the news hard to believe, but Jesus appeared to them, too. He showed them the wounds in his hands and feet and side. Then they knew the truth. Jesus had come back.

For forty days after his death, Jesus came to his disciples at different times. He told them that he would not be staying for ever but would return to God, his father. "But my father will send his Holy Spirit to you," Jesus told them. "Then you will be able to tell other people about me, here and all over the world."

One day, Jesus took his followers out of Jerusalem to a place called the Mount of Olives. As they watched, amazed, he seemed to be taken up into the sky. Two shining men, dressed in white, appeared and said, "Jesus has been taken up to heaven, but one day he will return."

Ten days later, the disciples gathered together to celebrate the Feast of Pentecost. Judas Iscariot was no longer with them. He had killed himself after he betrayed Jesus. The disciples chose another man, Matthias, to take Judas's place.

Suddenly, a sound like a rushing wind filled the whole house. To the disciples' astonishment, little tongues of flame appeared above their heads. Just as Jesus had promised, they were filled with God's Holy Spirit.

It was wonderful. The disciples found that they could speak foreign languages that they had never known before! They were ready to spread the news about Jesus just as their master had promised.

Seeing what had happened, and hearing the words of the disciples, more and more people came to believe in Jesus. They praised God and shared everything they had. Each day they met to pray together.

But just as in Jesus's time on Earth, the chief priests and the Roman leaders were worried by what was happening. These people were following a greater power than the rulers had themselves.

Spreading the Word

ACTS 3 : 1–10; 4 : 1–4; 6 : 8–15; 7 : 57–60; 8 : 1–2; 9 *onwards*

Jesus did many wonderful things during his time on Earth. Soon after he had been taken up to Heaven, the apostles (as his followers were now called) found that their Master was still doing wonderful things – through them!

One day, Peter and John came across a man begging by one of Jerusalem's gates. The man could not walk. Peter stopped. "I have no silver or gold to give you," he said, "but I will give you something else. In the name of Jesus Christ, walk!" The man jumped up and walked around!

Later, Peter explained to those who had heard about the miracle. "I didn't do this by myself," he said. "It was God who did it. He raised Jesus from the dead and now Jesus's name has cured this man."

Important officials were furious to hear this talk of Jesus being raised from the dead. They threw Peter and John into prison. But more and more people began to believe that Jesus really was the Son of God.

Soon all the apostles were healing people in Jesus's name, and doing other amazing things, too. They chose more men to help them with their work.

The authorities did their best to stop the apostles. A young man called Stephen became the first to be killed for his beliefs.

As Stephen was stoned to death, a man called Saul was watching. He was determined that talk about Jesus Christ must be stopped – and not just in Jerusalem. The news about Jesus was spreading far and wide. Saul set off for Damascus to hunt out believers there.

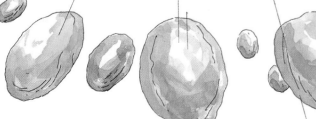

As Saul walked along the road, something extraordinary happened. A bright light suddenly shone all around him. The young man fell to the ground. He heard a voice, saying, "Saul, Saul, why are you trying to harm me?" It was Jesus! "Go on to Damascus," said the voice.

But when Saul stood up, he found he was blind. His companions had to lead him along the road to Damascus. For three days and nights, Saul did not eat or drink, but he did pray to God to show him what to do.

Jesus appeared to a man called Ananias in a dream. He sent Ananias to Saul to give him back his sight. Saul was a changed man. He asked to be baptized. Now he was as keen to help spread the word of Jesus as he had once been to stamp it out.

The apostles and their followers began to travel to tell more and more people about Jesus. Believers came to be called Christians. Saul was given a new name, too. He was now known as Paul.

For many years, Paul travelled. He helped new groups of Christians and wrote letters to those he could not see, guiding them in times of trouble. His journeys took him to Cyprus and Rhodes, to Malta and Sicily. He had many adventures. He was thrown into prison more than once and almost drowned when he was shipwrecked.

Finally, as a prisoner, Paul was taken to Rome. As he had been born in Tarsus, he was a Roman citizen, so at last he was released.

No one knows what happened to Paul in the end. He may have been killed when the Emperor Nero blamed Jews and Christians for a huge fire in Rome.

Whatever happened to Paul himself, his letters and teachings lived on as part of the Bible we know today. Although he was writing for people living in very different times and places, his messages about Jesus's love for all people are still read by Christians all over the world.

A Dream of the Future

REVELATION 21–22

There are many stories of dreams in the Bible. It was often in a dream that God spoke to men and women, showing them what he wanted them to do. The very last book of the Bible tells about a special dream that came to a man called John. Like many dreams, parts of it are mysterious and hard to understand, but it seems to say that Jesus is always with those who believe in him. The time will come when there will be no more death, or pain, or crying, and the light of God will fill every part of his kingdom for ever.